The Rumour

Contents

FULL FLIG

yay >>>

Titles in the Runway series

Level 4	Level 5	Level 6
The Street	Trapped	The Good Student
The Wish	The Rumour	Virtual Teacher
The Magic Shop	The Food Museum	Football Smash
The Ghost House	Escape from the City	The Empty House

Badger Publishing Limited
15 Wedgwood Gate, Pin Green Industrial Estate,
Stevenage, Hertfordshire SG1 4SU
Telephone: 01438 356907. Fax: 01438 747015
www.badger-publishing.co.uk
enquiries@badger-publishing.co.uk

The Rumour ISBN 978 1 84691 370 9

Text © Jillian Powell, Alison Hawes, Melanie Joyce 2008
Complete work © Badger Publishing Limited 2008

Publisher: David Jamieson
Commissioning Editor: Carrie Lewis
Design: Fiona Grant
Illustration: Seb Camagajevac, Robin Lawrie, Anthony Williams

Printed and bound in China through Colorcraft Ltd., Hong Kong

>» The Rumour

Written by Jillian Powell
Illustrated by Seb Camagajevac

One boy heard the rumour. He told his friend.

Soon, all the children heard the rumour.

The rumour went round the playground.
It went round the hall.
It went round the classroom.

The caretaker heard the rumour.
He told the dinner staff.

The rumour went round the staff room.

Someone rang the newspaper.
She told them the rumour.
She told them to come to the school after
dinner.

After dinner a big car came to the school.
Someone got out.
All the children and staff came to see.

The rumour was true.
The most famous footballer in the world
had come.
This was his old school.

Day Dreamer

Written by Alison Hawes
Illustrated by Robin Lawrie

Dawn looks at her school timetable.
Her first lesson is geography.

The teacher is talking about India.
Dawn dreams she is in India.

Soon, the whole class is in India too.

The bell rings.

"That was a good geography lesson!"
says everyone.

Dawn's next lesson is English.
In English, they are reading a play.
But Dawn dreams they are in the play....

The bell rings.
"We enjoyed that lesson!" says the class.

Dawn's next lesson is music.
Dawn dreams the class is singing on TV.

The bell rings.
"That was the best music lesson ever!"
says everyone.

Dawn's last lesson is science.
Her teacher is talking about the rainforest.

Dawn dreams she is in the rainforest.

Dawn looks at the beautiful birds and butterflies.

The bell rings.
"Where is everyone?" says Dawn.

School
Blues

Written by Melanie Joyce
Illustrated by Anthony Williams

Ana went to a new school.
She had a new blazer but it was too big.

Some girls went up to Ana.
"Your blazer is too big," said one girl.
"You look silly."

The school bell rang.
Ana didn't want to go in but she had to.

Ana was good at her lessons.
She liked English.
She liked Science.
She even liked Maths!

Some girls still didn't like Ana.
They said she was too good at her lessons.
They made fun of her.

Ana was good at football. She played for
the school team.
She scored goals and the team won.

Then the girls liked her.
They wanted to be her friends.

But now Ana had lots of friends.
She even had some football fans!

⏩ Vocabulary

The Rumour

rumour
guess
playground
hall
classroom
caretaker
staff
staff room
newspaper
famous

Day Dreamer

timetable
lesson
Geography
dreams
bell
English
play
Music
singing
Science

rainforest
birds
butterflies

School Blues

blazer
bell
silly
lessons
English
Science
Maths
team
scored
goals
fans

>>> Story questions

The Rumour

Who was first to hear the rumour?
Who told the dinner staff?
Why was the famous footballer at the school?

Day Dreamer

What was the class learning about in
Geography?
Why did the class disappear in science?
What would your 'dream' lesson be?

School Blues

Why did the other girls say that Ana looked
silly?
What sport was Ana good at?
Why was it hard for Ana to make friends?

R69077